Elizabeth I

MEG HARPER

A & C Black • London

For Judith Palka, passionate librarian and Tudor enthusiast,
and for all the other school librarians who do such fine work for young people

With special thanks to Professor Eric Ives

First published 2011 by
A & C Black Publishers Ltd
36 Soho Square, London, W1D 3QY

www.acblack.com

ISBN 978-1-4081-3119-0

A CIP catalogue for this book is available from the British Library.

This book is produced using paper that is made from wood grown in
managed, sustainable forests. It is natural, renewable and recyclable.
The logging and manufacturing processes conform to the
environmental regulations of the country of origin.

Printed and bound in Great Britain
by CPI Cox & Wyman, Reading RG1 8EX.

Contents

1

A Loyal Subject?

1549 Hatfield – Interrogation

Beneath her stiff, rich skirts, Elizabeth's legs were trembling. But she would not give way and sit down. She knew that Sir Robert Tyrwhitt's aim was to break her, to make her admit to some treasonous misdoing. If he succeeded, she might never see the familiar, cosy red-brick walls of Hatfield Palace again. Her very next words could be the ones to end her freedom – or even her life.

'Listen,' said Sir Robert. 'Your servants Astley and Parry are in the Tower. They have been interrogated.'

He raised an eyebrow and Elizabeth barely suppressed a gasp of alarm. Kate Astley had been her nurse since childhood and she could feel tears starting to her eyes at the thought that she was under arrest. But anger came to her aid. How dare they treat her servants like this? Or her, for that matter! She was the daughter of King Henry VIII! What right had anyone to try to intimidate her?

Her dark eyes flashed. 'And have they confessed to plotting against the Lord Protector?' she demanded. 'Because if they have, you have a duty to tell me. I think I should know if my servants are traitors!'

Sir Robert looked taken aback and Elizabeth felt a wave of satisfaction at his discomfort.

'No, your highness, they have confessed nothing,' he blustered. 'But they have told tales of... how shall I put it? Flirtation between you and Thomas Seymour. Now, what have you to say to that?'

Elizabeth made a dismissive gesture. 'Flirtation, Sir Robert?' she said. 'Have you never flirted yourself? Flirtation is no proof of a desire to marry, let alone to plot against the government! If that is all you have to accuse me of, then kindly stop wasting my time. I have told you already but I will say it again, I will never marry, either within England or out of England, without the consent of my brother, the King's majesty, and of the Lord Protector and the Council. Now please – let that be enough!'

Sir Robert's face was tight with frustration but he could not think what else to say to shake her. Elizabeth was only sixteen years old and yet she reminded him of her father – utterly self-possessed and determined. He knew when he was beaten.

Elizabeth flung herself back in her chair and watched the door close behind him with relief. What a very determined and crafty man he was! She hoped she had finally got rid of him – he had been sent by the Lord Protector to interrogate her, but she had given him nothing to report back. Was she safe at last? Had she managed to convince him that she had nothing to do with any plotting against her younger half-brother, the new boy king, Edward VI?

She sighed. What she would give for the company of her dear nurse – but Kate was locked in the Tower of London. And all because of the reckless, devious behaviour of Thomas Seymour, the younger brother of the very Lord Protector who demanded all this interrogation!

What an eventful time it had been since her father's death! She could scarcely believe all that had happened. At first, it had been peaceful enough. Elizabeth had gone to live with her father's widow, Catherine Parr. She loved Catherine, a woman still only in her thirties, intelligent and with similar interests to her own. As step-mothers went, she was as good as it got.

But then, events had helter-skeltered out of control. First Thomas Seymour had wanted to marry her or her sister Mary, but the Council had refused permission. Then, with King Henry barely dead, Thomas had married Catherine Parr. She had been in love with him before her marriage to Henry and was ready and willing – so Elizabeth found herself with a step-father who, just two months previously, had wanted to marry her! Worse, he still liked to flirt and tease her – in front of his new wife.

At first Catherine humoured his outrageous behaviour but finally she sent Elizabeth away. Elizabeth wasn't sure if she was relieved or disappointed but, as she had no choice, she tried to put the disturbing Thomas Seymour out of her mind.

And then, tragedy. Catherine died of childbed fever. Suddenly, to Elizabeth's astonishment, Thomas was back, proposing that she married him!

Elizabeth closed her eyes, her face flushed and her hands clammy. This part of her memories always upset her. There was no denying it, she had considered marrying Thomas. Though he was so much older than her, she felt very drawn to him. But she knew that he had made full enquiries about her finances, and she wasn't truly convinced of his love, or the virtue of his interest in her. When asked point blank if she intended to marry him, she was wary. She insisted that she would only do as the King's Council wished.

And how wise she had been! It made her stomach churn to think what might have happened otherwise. Along with plotting to marry her, it turned out that Thomas was also plotting to overthrow his older brother as Lord Protector.

When Thomas Seymour was arrested, suspicion of course fell on Elizabeth. What had been going on? Was she planning to marry Thomas and overthrow not just the Lord Protector but her half-brother, the King?

But Elizabeth was strong. No matter how Sir Robert Tyrwhitt tried to catch her out, she had insisted on her innocence. Even so, she wasn't safe. Thomas Seymour and her servants were still in the Tower. Tongues could still talk. And while she trusted Kate and Parry, she was not so certain of what Thomas Seymour would say about her.

She blinked hard. She must not crumple, however alone she felt. She had lost her father, a loved step-mother, and now all contact with her brother. Her half-sister Mary had never liked her. Their father, King Henry VIII, had divorced Mary's mother to marry Elizabeth's, Anne Boleyn – whom he had later had executed. Her two most trusted servants were in prison. There was no one to whom she could turn for comfort or help.

So... she must rely on herself. She mustn't give way to weakness. She had got through this crisis. If there were to be more, she must get through those too. She was the daughter of the most magnificent of English kings. She must survive.

1553 The Death of Edward

Elizabeth took up her pen. King though he was and loyal subject though she remained, she intended Edward to know that she was seriously put out. He was still her little half-brother, four years younger than she, and she didn't enjoy being treated so carelessly.

Really, it was too much! She had been looking forward to a short visit to court to brighten up the dull days of February, and now here she was, back at home! She had gone to all the trouble of having her servants pack everything up and set out, and then he had sent a messenger to meet them on the road to tell them her visit wasn't convenient after all. How rude! How inconsiderate! This was no way to treat an older sister, even if you were the King!

Elizabeth put down her pen again and considered. Something was going on, that was clear enough. Edward didn't want her at court right now. What was he trying to hide? What was he up to? She didn't like the influence the Duke of Northumberland and the Council had over her half-brother – he was still only fifteen, so couldn't rule entirely alone. Had they persuaded him to send her home? Or was he plotting something himself?

She knew he had very strong views of his own, not least about religion. The three of them, she, Edward and Mary, couldn't see eye to eye on this. Mary was profoundly Catholic whilst both Elizabeth and Edward were Protestants, but as far as Elizabeth was concerned, a person's religion should be a private matter. Her main concern was political stability and so long as the people's beliefs didn't threaten peace she was happy. Mary and Edward, however, both wanted everyone's religious practices to follow their own. Could Edward be planning some new religious law that he knew she wouldn't approve of?

Why did Elizabeth have a sense that all was not well? Everything was progressing just as her father, King Henry, had planned it, except that Edward was too young to rule alone. Now that the Duke of Northumberland was responsible for his care he was happier and healthier. He had had measles and smallpox the previous year but had recovered.

Or had seemed to. Maybe that was it. Maybe Edward was ill again and didn't want to worry her. Elizabeth felt a cold chill of dread seeping into her stomach. Worse, maybe Edward was so ill, he knew that he was dying – and then what would happen? The Catholic Mary was next in line to the throne. She would drag the country back into the Catholic faith, probably with the help of her friends in Spain – and what would that mean?

Elizabeth knew it would mean trouble – terrible trouble – and goodness knew what would happen to her in the midst of it! She would be seen as the Protestant rival to the Catholic Queen. Men would plot to put her on the throne – and if their plots misfired, she knew what that could mean. Death. She would be seen as a traitor and executed, half-sister to Mary or not.

Suddenly, she felt almost too sick to write.

She shook herself. This was silly. All that had happened was that Edward had said her visit was inconvenient, and here she was imagining all sorts of terrible possibilities! Probably Edward was not well but simply didn't want to worry her. They both knew how important it was for him to stay alive!

Elizabeth picked up her pen again and read what she had written. Yes, that would do. It was all very irritating but nothing to get so worked up about, she was sure.

It was a strangely quiet summer. Elizabeth saw nothing of either Edward or Mary. Edward was indeed ill, possibly with consumption. Elizabeth felt as if her life was on hold. God forbid that Edward died for if he did, everything would be thrown into turmoil.

It was late one night when the news came. A messenger had arrived, hot, sweaty and agitated after the long ride from London – would Elizabeth see him please?

'Fetch me my robe!' Elizabeth snapped. Moments later she was reading the dispatch.

Her brother was dead and – she sat down suddenly – her cousin Lady Jane Grey, the daughter of Henry VIII's younger sister, was proclaimed Queen!

'Your highness, you are not well!' said Kate, hurrying to her side. 'What has happened? Should I get you some wine – some ale?'

'No... no... I will be well in a moment. It is just... my brother is dead. Leave me, please. Leave me. I need some time alone.'

Respectfully, Kate and the messenger left but it was more than they could do not to discuss the matter.

'What has happened?' Kate demanded, as soon as she had provided the messenger with food and drink. 'The King is dead? But is that all?'

The messenger beckoned her closer. 'I only know the rumours,' he said in a low voice. 'It's said that Edward has named Lady Jane Grey as his successor – and has proclaimed that the Ladies Mary and Elizabeth have no claim at all!'

Kate had a sharp mind. 'He didn't want to be succeeded by a Catholic,' she gasped. 'So he has tried to rule out Mary. And he knows Elizabeth wouldn't agree to become Queen ahead of Mary – so he has ruled her out too!'

The messenger nodded. 'You may well be right. King Edward certainly didn't want all his efforts to make this a Protestant country undone.'

'Then these are dangerous times,' Kate said. 'The Lady Mary will not stand by and let this happen, I am sure.'

'Lord Robert Dudley has been sent to capture Lady Mary to stop her causing trouble – so they say,' said the messenger. 'I know nothing about what is to happen to Lady Elizabeth.'

Kate looked at the messenger keenly. 'Who sent you with this news?' she whispered.

'I cannot say,' said the man. 'But it is one who would not see the Lady Elizabeth harmed.'

Kate nodded and held her peace. It was best that she knew nothing.

2

Queen Mary

1553 – Queen takes Queen

Kate was right. These were indeed very dangerous times for Elizabeth. She sat tight at Hatfield whilst events unrolled. Mary evaded capture in the nick of time and gathered her supporters to march on London. Within days, she had toppled Lady Jane Grey, and her chief supporters were in the Tower, awaiting their fate. Mary might be Catholic, but she was a Tudor and the daughter of a popular King. The English people rallied behind her out of loyalty, disgusted by the attempt to disinherit her.

When it was clear that the immediate danger had passed, Elizabeth set off to join her in London, surrounded by two thousand of her own supporters. She needed to show her power – that she too could rally support, that she too was a splendid daughter of a great King – but also that she was graciously choosing to support her half-sister as the new monarch. She knew exactly how dangerous her situation was. Her sister could decide at any moment that she was too big a liability to be allowed to live. Even more dangerous was the will of the people, and Elizabeth wondered if Mary could retain their support. She swore to herself that if ever she became Queen, above all things she would keep her subjects' affection. She glanced sideways at her sister, so passionate about her Catholic religion, and wondered. Would Mary learn this lesson too?

1554 – Wyatt's Revolt

Elizabeth schooled her face into an expression of mild interest. She hoped her servant could not see her long fingers shaking as she refolded the letter from Queen Mary.

'That will be all, thank you,' she said. 'I will call for you when my reply is ready.'

The servant backed out courteously and Elizabeth sat down with relief. Her legs were trembling almost as much as her fingers. She read the letter again. It calmly explained that a rebellion had taken place, led principally by Sir Thomas Wyatt, but that it had mostly failed. The Queen urged Elizabeth to come and stay with her for own safety – she would be very welcome.

What was so alarming about that?

What the letter didn't mention was that the aim of the rebellion had been to topple Queen Mary and set Elizabeth up as Queen herself. Mary, foolishly in Elizabeth's view, was insisting on marrying Philip of Spain, a devout Catholic and heir to his father's empire. Elizabeth knew what the English people would think of that! They feared Philip as a Catholic but they also feared being absorbed into his Empire. Mary had made a terrible mistake in choosing Philip, and the Wyatt revolt was the result.

A summons now from Mary could mean only one thing – she thought Elizabeth was involved in Wyatt's plot and was taking her in for questioning. Elizabeth had no intention of going.

She took up paper and ink and wrote as innocently as Mary had to her, protesting that she felt too ill to travel and that it would be foolish for her to risk the journey since the country was so disturbed by rebellion. That, at least, should buy her some time.

'My lady, my lady!' Mrs Sandes rushed into Elizabeth's bedchamber, her voice urgent and fearful.

Elizabeth sat up hurriedly, clutching the bedclothes around her.

'Madam,' she said, sternly. 'Have some decorum, please! What is wrong?'

Mrs Sandes was a mature, experienced lady-in-waiting and she pulled herself together quickly.

'My lady, you must prepare yourself,' she said firmly. 'There are three privy councillors at the door and a troop of horsemen with them. They intend to take you to London, whether you like it or not.'

'Go down to them and say I am too ill to be moved,' said Elizabeth. 'Tell them that the journey would put me in peril of my life.'

Mrs Sandes looked at Elizabeth, who had been unwell for some days and had so little colour in her face that the blue veins stood out eerily. It was as good an argument as any.

'At once, your highness,' she said. 'You will stay in your bed, I take it?'

'Of course,' said Elizabeth. 'I feel far too ill to dress for these unexpected guests.'

She lay back. She did feel very ill indeed, sick with terror in fact. News of what was happening was not hard to come by. Queen Mary and her council had decided on a clampdown. The rebels were being rounded up and executed.

Her own father, Henry, had executed her mother, Anne Boleyn, along with Anne's brother and four other men he accused her of having had affairs with. Her brother Edward had executed his uncle, Sir Thomas Seymour. There was no reason to believe that Queen Mary would not execute her half-sister, even if they had been on fairly good terms for a while.

No one must know how scared she was. Fear suggested guilt and, above all, Elizabeth must seem innocent of any involvement in the latest plot. She was ill, that was all, and must not be moved.

1554 London – Prisoner

'Draw back the curtains!' Elizabeth demanded, sitting up in the litter that had been provided for her journey. Two doctors had insisted that she was well enough to travel and so she had had to go. It had taken nearly two weeks, because she had become much more sick whilst travelling, but she was finally entering London and was determined not to appear a shame-faced prisoner, hiding her face from the crowds. Instead, she sat proudly, a striking pale figure in white, surrounded by two hundred horsemen in red uniforms. No one watching could have guessed how much she was quaking inside.

Dreary anxious day followed dreary anxious day. Queen Mary, despite having arrested her, refused to see Elizabeth but kept her prisoner in a remote corner of Whitehall Palace, where she agonized over the events that were taking place outside her rooms. Seventeen-year-old Lady Jane Grey, who had reigned for thirteen short days before Mary took over, was cruelly executed along with her young husband. In these troubled times, they were seen as a risk. Elizabeth was only three years older. Clearly, her sister had no mercy when she felt threatened. All Elizabeth could do was wait and hope.

1554 Sent to the Tower

'I see,' said Elizabeth regally, after the Earl of Sussex had broken his news. 'If I am being sent to the Tower, I would like time to prepare myself, please.'

The Earl shook his head. 'Madam, my orders are that you must leave at once,' he said.

'In that case, I must be allowed to write to my sister,' said Elizabeth. 'It is unreasonable to hustle me in this way. I hope that is understood?'

The Earl looked at the Marquess of Winchester who had accompanied him. He gave a slight nod. 'Very well,' said the Earl. 'But make haste. Time and tide wait for no man. We travel by boat to the Tower and we cannot do it against the tide.'

'I will do my best,' said Elizabeth, haughtily. 'Now leave me, please!'

As soon as she was alone, apart from the guards at her door, Elizabeth sat down to write a letter on which might hinge her life. She appealed to the Queen as her sister and protested her innocence of any plotting, with Wyatt or anyone else. She sealed it with trembling fingers. Outwardly, she might seem haughty, but within her letter she had humbled herself. Her life was at stake and she would do whatever it took to save it.

By the time she had finished, the tide had turned and she couldn't make the journey to the Tower of London that night. But it did her no good. The Queen still refused to see her and was angry that she had been allowed to write.

Elizabeth stepped out of the boat at Tower Wharf the next day and crossed the bridge with her gaolers. She normally enjoyed a boat ride but today she felt queasy.

'What was that?' she asked anxiously as they made their way through the narrow passageways to the Tower. She had heard a sound so fearsome she wondered if it was a new sort of cannon.

'Have you forgotten the lions in the Royal Menagerie?' asked the Marquess. 'It is only their roaring.'

'And are all these men harnessed here for me?' Elizabeth asked, shocked by the number of guards. 'They aren't needed – I am only a weak woman.'

In fact, she intended to be strong. She knew she had many friends and supporters. But if her gaolers thought her weak, so much the better. Proving that she was no threat to Queen Mary was the only way to save her own life. Nonetheless, it was hard to stay brave as she passed the Bloody Tower and glimpsed the scaffold where, only days before, young Lady Jane Grey had been killed.

She was led to the royal palace that hid within the walls of the Tower. She hesitated on the threshold. Not for her a dank cell – instead a suite of rooms and attentive servants. But still she quailed at the thought of entering. This was where her mother, Anne Boleyn, had been imprisoned. And when her mother had left, it had been to take the short walk to the executioner's block.

Elizabeth drew in her breath. She had no choice. As the keys turned in the locks, she could only hope that her sister would be more merciful than her father had been.

3

Treason and Plots

1555 Woodstock Palace

Elizabeth drew in the reins of her horse sharply as a servant ran almost into her path.

'Have a care, man,' she cried. 'Would you have us both injured?'

'Your highness, there is a message come from the Queen, your sister. You are sent for at last. You are to go to Hampton Court at once.'

Two red dots of satisfaction burned in Elizabeth's pale cheeks. At last! Her imprisonment at the palace of Woodstock must be at an end. The year of dangerous plotting with supporters whilst keeping up an innocent front was over. But why? She frowned.

'Tell me,' she said, haughtily. 'Has the Queen's child been born?'

Elizabeth awaited the man's answer impatiently. If the Queen had a child, then she, Elizabeth, was no longer a threat to her throne.

The man shook his head. 'Nay, ma'am, but it is said that you are called to attend her during the confinement.'

The man was right. Elizabeth was indeed called to Hampton Court for the birth of Mary's baby and the long journey gave her plenty of time for reflection. When she had travelled to Woodstock after her release from the Tower, cheering crowds had supported her along her route. Now she was returning to London as if she were a rich nobody.

How had this come about? Her time imprisoned in Woodstock in rural Oxfordshire had been like living in another world. Yes, there had been plotting and even an attempt to overthrow Queen Mary, but Elizabeth and her supporters were little more than bothersome flies that Mary had ignored. The Queen had been absorbed with her own plot – to marry the Catholic King Philip II of Spain and to have a baby as soon as she could. She had pressed ahead with that, regardless of people's dismay, and now, despite her advanced years, she was expecting her baby to arrive at any moment.

'She probably pities me,' thought Elizabeth, curling her lip at the thought. 'She's probably brought me here to witness her triumph.'

Certainly it was bitterly hard to see the glorious gatehouse of Hampton Court Palace, so regal and elegant, golden in the spring sunshine, and then to enter from the back, as if she were a commoner. With a pang she looked around the panelled suite of rooms that had been occupied by her brother Edward and where she was now to stay, not too close to the Royal apartments. It was a change, however, from the oddness of Woodstock where she had lived a life of waiting, wondering what would happen next. Here everyone knew the answer to that. The Queen was going to have a baby.

Except that she didn't.

'Aaaarggh!'

The terrible groan of anguish drifted from the Queen's bedchamber across the little knot garden where Elizabeth was taking the air. She exchanged a wry grimace with Kate. The first time they had heard the dreadful cries, they had thought the baby was coming at last. Instead, every day, for several hours, the Queen sat on the floor, her knees drawn up, rocking in pain and anguish. Something was badly wrong. If she was pregnant, the baby should have arrived long ago. It seemed far more likely that Mary was suffering from a terrible illness which had swelled up her tummy like a cushion. The people of the court gossiped endlessly, some feeling great sadness for Mary, others thinking she was a fool. For Elizabeth, it meant just one thing. If there was no baby, she was still the next in line to the throne and the plotters would be at work. Her life was once again in danger.

1558 Hatfield – The Queen is dead

Elizabeth walked briskly through the park at Hatfield, her mind reeling. Her sister was dead. It had been expected but the shock was still intense. Nonetheless, she could not spare time to grieve. There was too much to think about.

The last few months had been very strange. As soon as it was known for sure that Mary had not been pregnant, Elizabeth's supporters had started plotting again. Her lips settled into a thin, determined line, her face unreadable. She would never reveal whether she was involved in their plots or not.

She knew she was lucky to be alive. She suspected that only Mary's husband, Philip II of Spain, had stood between her and execution. It was hard to understand why he had defended her but for Philip, the crucial thing was keeping England as his ally against France – so he wanted her on his side in case she ever became Queen.

Mary, probably spurred on by Philip, had tried to force Elizabeth into marrying the young Duke of Savoy, another Spanish ally, in order to keep her on side, but she had refused. Risky though it was, she was determined to stay in control of her own life. Philip might want her as a powerful ally in the future and it was lucky for her that he did – but she had no intention of being bossed around by a man, especially a foreigner!

She knew how much the people had hated Mary's marriage to Philip even though he had abandoned her painfully quickly and had returned to Spain. Elizabeth wouldn't take that risk. Above all things, she must keep the affection of the people. Mary had made them hate her, burning hundreds of Protestants, marrying Philip and dragging the country into war with France as well.

And now she was dead! It was hard not to feel relieved. They had had their better times, but in the last couple of years, Elizabeth had felt sure that Mary's hatred of her was growing. And why wouldn't it? She was popular, younger, prettier and healthier, as well as the daughter of Anne Boleyn.

Despite it all, Mary had named Elizabeth as her heir. Elizabeth knew all too well that Philip expected her to be grateful to him and a good ally as a result. But she had told his envoy exactly what she thought of that. Philip might have had influence over Mary – but it was the people who would swing the day. If they wanted her to be Queen, she would be Queen. And she would choose for herself whether she wanted Spain as an ally.

Elizabeth turned and started to walk briskly back towards the palace. Her ladies were hovering at a distance, chattering. Well, there was much to chatter about! But wait – others were approaching.

A group of men had stopped to talk with the women.

Elizabeth drew herself up regally. She knew who they would be and she swept forward to greet them. Her own spies had been busy. She had known for some time that Mary was dead but here were her councillors come to tell her so.

Seeing her advancing, they fell to their knees on the grass. Graciously she let them present their news and expressed her sorrow, such as it was. Then, she asked them to rise and addressed them in clear confident tones.

'Gentlemen, in this task laid before me, I will need your assistance, chiefly you of the nobility,' she said, 'that I with my ruling and you with your good service may make a good account to Almighty God. I mean to direct all mine actions by good advice and counsel.'

Then she dismissed them. Let them go and worry about whether they would remain on her Council or not. She had much to think about and organise now that she was Queen.

4

No Man Good Enough?

1560 Windsor – Did she fall or was she poisoned?

Elizabeth reined in her horse and paused to wait for the man galloping behind her.

'Enough for today?' he asked, drawing in his own horse beside her.

Elizabeth shook her head. 'When have I ever had enough of riding or hunting?' she asked. 'You have known me since I was a little girl, Robin!'

'So...?' The question was evident in his tone. Why had they stopped?

'I need to talk to you privately,' said Elizabeth, 'and opportunities to be completely private at court are rare. You know how people talk.'

Robert Dudley knew only too well. The court was full of gossip about his relationship with the

Queen, especially now that she had made him Master of Horse which, of all the jobs in her council, was the one which gave him the most time in her company. They were lovers, they were secretly engaged, Elizabeth had had a child by him – the rumours were rife because the Queen so obviously enjoyed his company. And he enjoyed hers. So why didn't they marry? The country needed an heir to the throne – no one wanted a return to the turmoil of the past. If only she could produce a child, Elizabeth, popular and successful as she was, would seem the perfect Queen.

There was one big stumbling block: Robert's wife, Amy, who spent most of her time at their home in Oxfordshire whilst Robert was at court. Amy was ill, and it was partly this that kept her at home and Robert free to be Elizabeth's companion.

Now Elizabeth turned to Robert gravely.

'I have heard,' she said in a low voice, 'that your wife has taken a turn for the worse. Is this true?'

Robert nodded. 'I'm afraid so.'

'Is she dying?' Elizabeth asked.

'I fear that she is.'

'Then perhaps you should go to her,' said Elizabeth. 'I can spare you for a short while.'

Robert shook his head. 'She could be as she is for many months. If there is a crisis, I will be sent for.'

Elizabeth looked irritated. 'Foolish boy!' she snapped. 'It reflects badly on me, the Queen, if I appear to be keeping a man away from his dying wife.'

'I am sure there is no crisis,' said Robert, soothingly, 'but if I get word that there is, I will go at once, of course.'

It was a damp, wet day when the news came. Elizabeth was sitting with her ladies, working at her embroidery, occasionally glancing through the tiny window panes, willing the September sun to emerge and light up the pale oak panelling which lined the room and which now looked drab and oppressive. She longed to throw aside her sewing and get out on a horse but even she saw the sense in not getting her heavy clothing wet.

The messenger arrived hot-foot. He had thrown aside his jerkin but his undergarments were damp from the heavy rain and he had a distinct aroma of the stableyard.

Elizabeth, who hated strong smells, waved him away at once.

'You do not need to stand beneath my nose for me to hear you,' she said, haughtily. 'Speak from the door.'

'News from my Lord Dudley, your Majesty,' the man said. 'My Lady Dudley is dead.'

There was a chorus of gasps from the ladies. Elizabeth herself flinched but compressed her lips so that no sound escaped her.

'How did this happen?' she asked. 'Had the course of her illness reached its close?'

'Your majesty, I don't know,' said the messenger, 'but my lady was found dead at the foot of the great staircase of Cumnor Place when the servants returned from Abingdon Fair.'

The ladies gasped again.

'Perhaps she was pus....'

'Silence!' snapped the Queen, her dark eyes flashing. 'We will have no idle talk here! See that this man is dried and fed and a bed is found for him before he returns. Ladies, you may leave me now.'

Silently, not daring to murmur their suspicions, the ladies gathered up their work and left the room, leaving Elizabeth to her troubled thoughts.

She was in turmoil. She paced the floor and then stood at the window, staring out at the miserable sky. So Amy Dudley was dead. Robert, she knew, was here at court. He could have had no direct part in it. He could, of course, have hired a killer, and that was a side of Robert that she chose to ignore. He was not popular – few people seemed to like him, and there were those who slandered him by suggesting he was adept with poison. But Amy had been dying anyway. If he had wanted to marry Elizabeth, all he had to do was wait.

Now, however, his fate was sealed and so was hers. They could not marry. If they did, whatever the truth of the matter, it would look as if Robert had killed his wife in order to marry the Queen. Or worse, that she herself had arranged for Amy's death. No, there was no choice. However attractive she found him, however much she loved his companionship, she could never marry Robert Dudley. Maybe that solved a dilemma for her. In so many ways she was better off without a husband to tell her what to do and to play the King. Mary had suffered that from Philip, even though he had abandoned her and gone back to Spain.

Elizabeth stared out of the window thinking of the joyous times she had spent in Robert's company. She sighed deeply. She would keep him as her dear companion, but never as her husband. And whatever her council said, however much they wanted her to bear a child, she thought that being a single queen, a virgin queen, might suit her very well indeed.

1562 Hampton Court – Smallpox

Elizabeth could barely open her eyes for the scabs that clustered around her eyelids. Her head ached dully and she felt so weak she could scarcely raise a hand. Not that she wanted to. She shrank at the thought of her hands, covered in lumpy pustules and scabs. They had been beautiful, long and elegant with tapering fingers. She could only hope that the smallpox scars were not too disfiguring. Her face could be covered in thick white make-up but her hands? She had many beautiful gloves but even so, how she hoped that the scarring would not be too terrible! She might not want a husband but the thought that a man might find her ugly was too painful. Once again, she slipped away into the restless sleep of a high fever, too ill to string any more thoughts together.

'You look exhausted, Cecil,' said Elizabeth, gazing up at her First Secretary languidly

Sir William Cecil bowed respectfully. The scabs of her dreadful illness had fallen away and there was no longer any danger of infection, or indeed, of her death. He was overwhelmed with relief. He was an experienced court official and had known Elizabeth for several years before she had become Queen and appointed him her principal secretary. He still felt ill when he thought of that terrifying moment when she had collapsed at Hampton Court and had remained unconscious for a whole day. The skilled doctor they had sent for had refused to come. But for a devoted servant who threatened to kill him with a dagger if he did not do so, the Queen could have died! The doctor himself admitted it had almost been too late.

Lying propped up in her massive bed, Elizabeth still looked thin and frail. It would be unwise to say so, however.

'Your majesty, it is such a pleasure to see you well again,' Sir William said tactfully. 'We were in great terror for your life.'

This was to put it mildly. Sir William had called an emergency meeting of the Council, convinced that they must urgently find an heir to the throne. It had been impossible to agree on anyone suitable and Sir William had scarcely slept for days whilst the Queen moaned and cried out in a desperate fever before the horrible smallpox rash broke out and covered her. Now the Council insisted that as soon as possible she must call Parliament so that they could persuade her of the urgent need to marry and have a child. There were several possible candidates – Erik XIV of Sweden, her sister Mary's widower Philip II, one of the Archdukes of Austria – but Cecil was sure Elizabeth would have none of them, even if, to please Parliament, she flirted with the idea of marriage.

'You see that I am well on the way to recovery,' said Elizabeth. 'Were you here on a friendly visit?'

Sir William took a deep breath. 'Your majesty, it would be well if you would call Parliament as soon as you are able to, please. There is much that must be discussed.'

'The question of my marriage, for example,' said Elizabeth coolly.

'Well, yes, indeed,' said Sir William. 'We were terrified that we would lose you. Without a clear heir, we could have civil war again.'

'Yes, thank you, Sir William, I have not lost my brain during my illness,' Elizabeth snapped. 'I do know the problems that we face.'

'So... will you call Parliament soon?' Sir William asked, greatly daring.

'I will do what it pleases me to do when it pleases me to do it,' said Elizabeth. 'As you can see, I am not yet well enough to leave my bed – and I wish you and the members of my Parliament would remember what I have told you.'

'That you are happy to live and die a virgin?' said Sir William, his face downcast.

'Indeed. But I will consider the matter again. I appreciate that my present illness has given everyone great cause for alarm – I know that a Catholic monarch is feared just as much as civil war. But you must also consider how very influential any husband of mine might be. I do not think the common people would want me to marry a foreigner, do you? Especially not another Spaniard. Nothing is simple about this, Sir William – and bear in mind that I would have to live with the man!'

'Indeed, ma'am,' said Sir William, bowing his head respectfully. 'But please remember that if anything happened to you, our choice would not be easy. Lady Catherine Grey, the Earl of Huntingdon, or, God forbid, your cousin, Mary – and she has much support amongst Catholics.'

Elizabeth nodded graciously. 'Thank you for reminding me, Sir William,' she said. 'Now please take your leave. I am weary.' She held out her hand for him to kiss, a hand that was gratifyingly free of scars.

Elizabeth lay back on her pillows as Cecil left. Her cousin. The one they called Mary Queen of Scots, but who was convinced she should also be Queen of England. What a nuisance that woman was! A Catholic revolt to snatch the throne for her could easily happen – and she was too silly and thoughtless for that to be allowed.

Elizabeth shut her eyes. She was too weak to try to think of a solution that didn't involve beheading her cousin. Right now, marrying Erik of Sweden was tempting – he had lavished gifts on her of gold and piebald horses. But in her heart, Elizabeth knew that was not what she wanted. She had survived to become Queen and she wanted to *be* Queen, not someone playing at it while her husband took the real control. She did not want to be the underling of any man, not even Robert. Parliament would just have to get used to that idea – and in the end, something might have to be done about Mary Queen of Scots. But Elizabeth hoped not.

5
The Queen of Scots Problem

1563 – That Dangerous Woman

'Your majesty cannot be serious!'

Lord Robert Dudley stared at the Queen in consternation.

Elizabeth smiled grimly. 'Indeed I am, Robin,' she said. 'I cannot marry you myself after your wife died in such odd circumstances – and there is great need for my cousin to be safely married to an English lord who is loyal to me. You would be ideal!'

Lord Robert tried to control his features and his tongue.

'Your majesty, I think that is perhaps asking a little too much of my love and loyalty.'

Elizabeth rose to her feet. 'Really?' she said in an arctic voice. 'Can too much ever be asked of a loyal and loving subject by his Queen?'

Lord Robert's handsome face flushed darkly and he threw back his shoulders angrily. The Queen was tall but he appeared to tower over her.

'I take my leave of you, ma'am,' he said.

'Do,' said Elizabeth. 'You will hear more from me on this matter, however.'

'You are troubled, your majesty?'

Elizabeth was sitting brooding, her pen in her hand, a pile of letters before her. She started at Kate Astley's voice and turned.

'Ah, Kate,' she said. 'Do you think Robert will wed my cousin as I have suggested? Do you think she will accept him? The English crown would be so much safer if such a marriage took place!'

Kate pursed her lips. 'Hmm,' she said. 'Forgive me if I cannot agree with you, your majesty, but in my view the English crown would be much safer if you married yourself and had a child before it is too late. But you have heard me say so many a time and will take no notice.'

'Kate, you would have me wed Robert and you know that I cannot! Some people think that he murdered his wife!'

'Not many,' said Kate, 'and people forget. Especially in the joy of a wedding and a birth. Tell me, your majesty – how would you feel to see Lord Robert married to that dangerous woman?'

Elizabeth turned away again, hiding her expression. 'I would rejoice that the English crown was safe from the threat of a Catholic queen,' she said, firmly.

'Hmmph!' muttered Kate, but under her breath so the Queen could not hear. She knew that in Elizabeth's bed-chamber, tucked away in a cabinet, there lay hidden a miniature portrait of Robert, wrapped in paper and labelled 'My Lord's Picture'. And the Queen was intending to marry him off to her cousin!

1565 Windsor Castle

Elizabeth had been riding all day, so fast and hard that her ladies, less robust and keen than she, were exhausted. It was a relief to them when she finally turned for home and they trotted wearily back towards Windsor Castle. Elizabeth had been sullen and quiet for hours. It was now over a week since Kate Astley had died and Elizabeth was still grief-stricken. Kate had been her companion for most of her life and the loss had hit her hard. But there was worse news awaiting her.

'Mary has married Lord Darnley! And proclaimed him King of Scotland! It cannot be true! This is terrible!' Elizabeth's dark eyes were alive with shock and fury.

'I'm afraid it is true,' said Lord Robert. 'The news has just arrived from Lord Murray, her half-brother.'

'But Lord Darnley has a claim to the English throne as good as hers! Together they could have a child and... Robin, you should have married her!'

'Your majesty, you could not force her to marry me. Clearly she has ideas of her own. She wants to be Queen of England, not to be a puppet controlled by you. So she has married someone who will help her – or so she thinks.'

'What will I do if they have a child?' said Elizabeth, showing dangerous signs of the hysteria to which she sometimes gave way. 'Oh, this is a disaster, Robin!'

'Perhaps, your majesty, you should do what all your councillors advise you to do and marry yourself,' said Lord Robert, not daring to look the Queen fully in the eye. 'Your child would have a greater claim to the throne than hers.'

There was a terrifying silence in which Elizabeth was clearly battling to control herself.

'And you, I suppose, would like to be the father of that child?' said Elizabeth at last.

Lord Robert said nothing. He didn't dare.

'Well,' said the Queen. 'We shall see. You may go.'

As soon as he had gone, Elizabeth threw herself down in a chair, put her head in her hands and screamed.

1566 Greenwich Palace – A Son for the Queen

It was a pleasant summer evening and the Queen was staying at her palace in Greenwich. Supper had been eaten and she and her ladies and some courtiers were dancing when Sir William Cecil arrived by boat.

What could be so important that he had set out along the river at this hour? The musicians paused but the Queen waved to them to carry on and Sir William made his entrance quietly. Even so all eyes watched as he whispered something to the Queen. She staggered to a chair and sat down. Immediately, her ladies gathered round her, all bustle and concern.

'The Queen of Scots has had a son,' she gasped, 'and I am barren!'

It was not like the Queen to give way to weakness in public for long, although those who were intimate with her grew used to seeing her fits of hysteria when she was under particular stress. On this occasion she quickly pulled herself together and, the next morning, when she received Lord Melville who had brought the news from Scotland, she bounded forwards eagerly.

'May I congratulate you on being the bearer of such happy news!' she said. 'Please convey my earnest good wishes and congratulations to Mary, my cousin.'

'And are you happy to be the child's god-mother, your majesty?' enquired Lord Melville, with some trepidation. He had been told of the Queen's breakdown on hearing the news and was wary of her reaction. It was as if she didn't know her own mind – apparently so reluctant to marry and yet so upset to hear about the birth.

Elizabeth, however, had her feelings under control now. No one would ever know if she was jealous, if she regretted the course she consistently chose, if really she longed for marriage and children. She would school herself to hide her feelings and do what was best for her people and the monarchy, whatever she believed that to be.

'Naturally,' she assured Lord Melville, 'though of course, someone will have to stand proxy for me. I cannot send an English lady north at this time of year but the Duchess of Argyll will be happy to oblige us, I'm sure. And I must be allowed to provide the font – silver-gilt, I think. I will arrange for it to be made and sent.'

Lord Melville bowed low in acknowledgement. It was little wonder that the Queen commanded such respect, he thought. Whatever distress her cousin's news had caused her, there was no sign of any jealousy, resentment or bitterness now. She was all smiles and enthusiasm. Clearly, she had a will of iron and the intelligence to know how to apply it. She had survived the suspicions of both Edward and Mary and he had little doubt that she would survive the plots of any other pretenders to the throne – including, should she be so tempted, those of Mary, Queen of Scots.

Mary was Elizabeth's cousin, but had none of her self-control. She was a woman who seemed to attract scandal. Even now there was gossip of the most shocking kind about her. It was said that Mary was tired of her young husband Darnley and had become great friends with her Italian secretary David De Rizzio, whom the Protestant lords of Scotland believed was helping her plot to make Scotland a Catholic country. Together with Darnley, the Scots lords had killed De Rizzio before her eyes. She was lucky she had not lost her baby as a result of the shock.

It was all extremely disturbing. When Parliament met again in September, the members were even more determined that Elizabeth should marry.

'You promised last session that you would give us an answer on this matter,' insisted the Duke of Norfolk, the highest ranking noble in the land.

Elizabeth was alarmed. She was not prepared for this.

'Have I not governed you well so far?' she exclaimed. 'What need is there for the interference of someone else in these matters?'

Somehow the end of the session was reached but all was in disorder and tempers ran so high that some of the members came to blows. The Queen withdrew but not before the lords had insisted on an audience with her. Lord Robert was among them.

The Queen was furious. She did not mince her words, even abusing Lord Robert.

'You know my feelings on this, Robin,' she said. 'And I had thought that even if all the world abandoned me, you would not!'

Lord Robert turned pale.

'Your majesty, I would do anything for you,' he retorted. 'You know I would die at your feet if I had to!'

Elizabeth curled her lip. 'And pray tell me,' she said. 'How would that help right now?'

The quarrel dragged on. The Queen had never been more angry with Parliament nor they more frustrated with her. In the end, she gave them a little hope. She would marry she said, 'when it was convenient'. With this, they had to be satisfied. There was still no obvious choice. Besides, Mary Queen of Scots was in no position to take the English throne, struggling as she was to keep the sympathy of the Scottish lords. And then something happened that made them completely turn against Mary. Her husband, Lord Darnley, was murdered.

6
Murder and Conspiracy

1567 – London

'What? Can this be true?'

The messenger nodded. 'It is the talk of Edinburgh and Glasgow,' he said.

The Queen turned to her ladies.

'Lady Howard, Lady Cecil, you must go to Lady Lennox at once,' she said.

The ladies immediately began gathering their sewing together.

'Why does she need us?' asked Lady Cecil.

'You must break terrible news to her,' said the Queen. 'Her son, Lord Darnley, King of Scots, is dead.'

A shocked murmur ran round the chamber.

'But he was so young,' said Lady Howard. 'And so recently made King! How has this come about, your majesty?'

'He has been murdered,' said Elizabeth, 'or so it would appear. He was ill at Kirk o'Field – I know not from which illness he suffered – but in the night, there was an explosion in the house. Gunpowder had been set – it was no accident – but Darnley's body was found in the garden. It would seem that he was suffocated.'

'What? Someone strangled him as well as blowing up his house?' gasped Lady Howard. 'Who would do such a thing?'

The silence was as thick as the heavy bedspreads the ladies were embroidering. They all knew that Mary Queen of Scots had come to loathe her husband.

'She could not have done it alone,' a lady murmured. 'She must have had help.'

'Silence!' snapped Elizabeth. 'There is no suggestion that the Queen of Scots had any part in this. She and her husband both have many enemies. I will not have my cousin slandered!'

The lady who had spoken flushed painfully and curtsied low before withdrawing into a corner. But as the days wore on, it became obvious that the young woman was right.

'It would appear,' explained Sir William Cecil, 'that the Scottish lords were in favour of disposing of Lord Darnley.'

'So are they happy with the result then?' demanded Elizabeth, her face pinched with disgust.

'No, indeed, your majesty,' said Sir William, 'for your cousin appears to have taken up with the Earl of Bothwell, he who is suspected of murdering Darnley, and there are rumours that she will marry him next. She has gone to a house-party where he is known to be staying.'

'She has gone to a house-party!' exclaimed the Queen. 'But her husband has scarcely been dead a week! I cannot credit such idiocy! It cannot be true!'

'On the contrary,' said Sir William. 'It is all too true.'

'She must have this murder investigated properly,' said Elizabeth. 'She needs to clear her name. It is no good trying to turn a blind eye to it. This is urgent. I must write to her at once!'

'Very good, your majesty,' said Cecil, 'but I fear you will be wasting your ink.'

Sir William was right. Mary was too much in love to take any notice of Elizabeth's advice and Bothwell's trial was barely worthy of the name. No sooner had it finished than he pretended to 'abduct' Mary. She was more than willing to go with him, and married him as soon as he had divorced his wife. In this one rash blow, Mary alienated the Scottish lords and common people, Elizabeth, and all the European princes who had thought she would make a useful wife.

Nor did it lead to happiness for her. She and Bothwell were universally loathed, and uprisings against them soon began. Elizabeth, despite being furious that her cautions had been ignored, did what she could to help. Mary was still part of her family, she still wanted peace in Scotland and she was concerned for the safety of Mary's baby son.

But there was nothing she could do. Mary's forces met those of the Scottish lords at Carberry Hill but disbanded without fighting. At the end of the day, Bothwell fled and Mary never saw him again. She, meanwhile, was taken captive and had to brave the jeers of the mob in Edinburgh before being imprisoned in the island castle of Lochleven.

1567 – On the Rack

'So where can we find evidence of this plot?' demanded Dr Wilson, the Master of the Court of Requests. There had been other plots against Elizabeth's life, and torture had played a large part in unravelling them. But this new plot was complex and difficult to pin down. Warnings had come in from various sources – Elizabeth was developing a very powerful espionage network, headed by Sir Francis Walsingham – and it seemed that an Italian banker named Roberto Ridolfi had been plotting to overthrow Elizabeth for several years. He had been working to find foreign contacts to help.

Slowly, the truth was being pieced together. The plan appeared to be that the Duke of Alba would invade from the Netherlands with 10,000 men, incite a rebellion in the north of England, murder Elizabeth, and marry Mary Queen of Scots to Thomas Howard, Duke of Norfolk. But more proof was needed – and the fine detail – before the conspirators could be arrested and tried. Hence the merciless interrogation.

The man strung out on the rack, one of the Duke of Norfolk's secretaries, shook his head and groaned. Sweat dripped from his face and his ribs looked ready to burst through his stretched flesh.

Dr Wilson nodded at the man turning the wheel.

'A little more persuasion, I think,' he said. 'We nearly have what we want.'

As the rack wrenched the man's taut body, he emitted a cry of agony.

'Stop, stop,' he gasped. 'There's a place – a hiding place – there are letters...'

Dr Wilson smiled grimly. 'Tell me more,' he said.

Minutes later, he knew exactly where to find the letters which would tell the spymasters all they needed to know about Ridolfi's plot to kill Elizabeth and set up Mary Queen of Scots on the English throne. Walsingham would be pleased – he made no secret of the fact that he believed Elizabeth's life would be at risk until the Queen of Scots was dead, and Wilson suspected that Burghley felt the same. Perhaps the uncovering of this plot would be the end of her – one could only hope. But Wilson suspected that it would take a lot more than this for Elizabeth to allow the execution of her cousin.

For her, it was a crime for a Queen to kill a Queen, and much worse if that Queen happened to be her cousin.

1572 London – Stay of Execution

Elizabeth could not sleep. She tossed and turned in her great bed until her night shift was tangled and sweaty. It was no use. She would have to act, despite the lateness of the hour. She threw back her covers, pulled her robe around herself and called for a messenger.

'Take this note to Lord Burghley immediately,' she told the young man, who stood sleepily in front of her.

'Lord Burghley?' he said.

'Yes, Lord Burghley, Sir William Cecil that was! Don't you know I have made him a lord? Well, never mind – just go as quickly as you can!'

The messenger hurried off and Elizabeth threw herself back on the bed to wait, but she could not settle. She prided herself on avoiding wanton cruelty. Yes, she allowed torture to be used when matters of the utmost importance were at stake, but in matters of personal conscience she was prepared to be tolerant. A man's religious faith should be his own private business – providing it did not lead him into disloyalty to his Queen and country. In this she differed from her sister and brother, who had both felt bound to force their own religious views on their subjects – and she was convinced she was right to do so.

But Norfolk, her trusted subject for so many years, had gone wildly astray, led into treasonous plotting by his infatuation with her cousin and the pull of his family's long-standing Catholicism. His life was forfeit – she knew it was. And yet she hesitated. She was not a cruel woman – she was a tolerant one. It grieved her terribly to behave otherwise, however vital it was. When Burghley arrived, he found her anxiously pacing her room.

'It is about the Duke of Norfolk,' she said. 'His execution tomorrow must be stopped.'

Burghley suppressed a sigh. 'Again, your majesty? You have already postponed his execution once and it has been proved beyond doubt how deeply he was involved in Ridolfi's plot. He would have married your cousin, Mary.

He would have been King! You cannot let this man live – it isn't safe!'

'Burghley, my own mother was executed. I lived in fear of execution as a young girl. My sister Mary burned many people at the stake and was hated as a result, and rightly so! The Duke of Norfolk is a fool and I believe has been misled by minds more evil than his own. He must not be executed tomorrow.'

'Your majesty, you allowed his servants to be tortured in order for this plot to be unveiled. Why hold back at punishing the ringleader?'

'He was not the ringleader! That much is obvious!' snapped the Queen. 'And torture is not execution! Now leave me – and make sure my orders are carried out tomorrow. The Duke of Norfolk is not to die.'

'Parliament will not like it,' sighed Burghley.

'Parliament is not the Queen,' retorted Elizabeth.

Burghley withdrew. He knew there was no arguing with Elizabeth in this mood. But he feared for her future. Until Mary Queen of Scots was dead, Elizabeth would never be safe. It was a bad day when the Scottish queen had escaped from her prison at Lochleven and Elizabeth had taken pity on her. She was kept under house arrest but that simply made her seem like a damsel in distress to the foolish men who fell under her spell. The Duke of Norfolk was not the only idiot to adore her.

Elizabeth needed to be more ruthless. Her belief that a man's religion was his own affair made her too tolerant, in his view, and therefore vulnerable. There would be plots and more plots to put Mary on the throne, Burghley was sure. This had been just the first of many.

7
Marriage Matters

1575 Warwickshire

Lord Robert Dudley bowed low over the Queen's hand and kissed it elegantly before he led her into the colossal tent which had been pitched at Long Itchington for her refreshment and entertainment.

Elizabeth, although she never had a large appetite, exclaimed at the sight of the sweetmeats laid out inside.

'Robin, this is magnificent,' she said.

Lord Robert smiled. 'It is only the start of the delights that await you at Warwick and Kenilworth,' he said. 'My brother and I plan to make this the most magnificent entertainment you will ever experience on a summer progress.'

'I trust I won't have such evil news as I received the last time I was at Kenilworth,' said Elizabeth, her face darkening.

'Indeed, your majesty, I hope not too,' said Lord Robert.

Just three years ago, it was at Kenilworth that she had learnt of the terrible Massacre of St Bartholomew, in which crazed Catholics in Paris had turned on the Protestants and killed them by the hundred, even children and babies. Scores of Protestants had fled to England and Elizabeth was delighted by all that they contributed with their great skills with textiles. But now the English people were even more terrified of Catholics and therefore of Mary Queen of Scots, and of Elizabeth herself marrying a foreign Catholic. For Elizabeth and her ministers, protecting England from war, and from falling into Catholic hands once she was dead, was a constant worry.

For now, however, Elizabeth had over two weeks to enjoy herself at the expense of Robert and his brother, the Earl of Warwick, and she certainly meant to do so.

The first delight was the discovery that Robert had added a whole new building to the castle at

Kenilworth, especially to house the Queen and her party. It was full of sumptuous four-poster beds, decked out in rich hangings of crimson, green, peach and white, trimmed with gold and silver lace or fringing. Even the stools holding the pewter chamber pots were padded with quilted black velvet. New-fangled glass was everywhere – candlesticks, serving dishes, windows – the place twinkled and glittered in the evening sunshine.

And then, what festivities there were! Day after day of firework displays, hunting, masques and plays, bear-baiting and country sports. When the weather turned foul there were indoor amusements a-plenty, amongst them an astonishing aviary of exotic birds, made to look as if it was encrusted with jewels.

The highlight was a water-pageant on the lake which bounded the castle, a clever mixture of music and spectacular drama, in which the Lady of the Lake appeared to advance on her floating island, accompanied by an enormous mermaid perched on a giant dolphin.

Elizabeth was delighted, not just because she loved theatre, pageantry and music, but because all this made work for her subjects, kept them out of mischief, and ensured she was very much before their eyes and in their hearts. That theatre and the arts thrived through her interest and care was a wonderful bonus.

It was all utterly enchanting. Who could doubt that Lord Robert Dudley was still her devoted lover, even though she refused to marry him?

Who could have guessed that he was playing a double game – keeping the favour of the queen whilst his attentions were turning to someone else?

Nothing seemed to trouble the great Kenilworth festival apart from a couple of days of rain. There were no accidents, unlike during a previous progress to Warwick when a firework had gone astray and burnt down someone's house! Finally, the whole festival was followed by a series of visits to great country houses with Robert acting as the tour guide. His only interest seemed to be Elizabeth's pleasure and her safety from the heat and smells of London.

Who could have suspected otherwise?

1578 London – The Queen's Pain

Elizabeth lay in her bed racked with pain. She had not slept for two days and looked heavy-eyed and wan. Her advisors crowded around the bed anxiously.

'The renowned tooth-drawer Fenatus says there is no hope for the tooth,' said Lord Burghley. 'He could make a potion of fennygreek to paint on the tooth and make it fall out – but it could affect the teeth either side as well. He recommends that you have the bad tooth pulled out.'

Elizabeth shook her head. 'Never,' she said. 'I could not bear it.'

The men looked perplexed. Her ladies muttered. They had known only too well what her reaction would be – they had been trying to nurse her through this latest bout of terrible toothache.

'Your majesty, you are brave and have suffered many things,' persisted Lord Burghley, 'and Jehan de Simier is likely to arrive in a few days and you know how vital it is that his visit goes well.'

Elizabeth groaned and turned her head sideways on her pillows. She knew all about Simier's visit and its importance. He was the representative of the Duke of Alençon, the younger son of the French king, whom she was pretending to plan to marry. In fact, she had no intention of doing so – he was twenty-one and she was forty-five – but the longer the French believed her to be seriously interested the better. They could hardly invade Scotland, support Mary Queen of Scots or join Spain in a joint attack on England, if they thought she was going to marry their prince! She had to look young and well and lively for the visit. But she simply couldn't bear the prospect of having a tooth pulled out. She had never lost a tooth before. However much wine she drank, she knew it wouldn't deaden the pain entirely.

'Your majesty, we have a skilled surgeon with us,' coaxed Lord Burghley. 'It would be the work of a moment.'

But Elizabeth still refused.

Then an older man stepped forward. It was John Aylmer, the Bishop of London, and one of Elizabeth's life-long supporters.

'Your majesty,' he said. 'There is nothing to fear. I have had many a tooth drawn and have few left.

But any I have are entirely at your majesty's service. The surgeon will pull out one of mine now, to show you that it is no great matter.'

With that, he took a seat, nodded to the surgeon and within moments, he was one tooth the less! The surgeon brandished it high and smiled at the stunned Queen.

'You see,' he cried. 'There is nothing to fear!'

With such devotion and kindness shown her, Elizabeth could no longer refuse. The surgeon advanced, her ladies came to hold her hands, and seconds later, the bad tooth was gone. There was a polite round of applause and her advisors withdrew, smiling in relief and murmuring over this feminine delicacy in one normally so tough. Elizabeth slept meanwhile and, when Simier arrived, was her usual spirited but haughty self.

He was charming and an excellent negotiator for the Duke – but the months passed and still no marriage contract was sealed. It was all a clever, diplomatic game but, of course, the secret had to be carefully kept – even from Lord Robert. He made it clear that he could not bear the idea of Elizabeth giving her hand to someone else by spreading nasty rumours about Simier. He also tried to persuade Elizabeth that if she married Alençon, she would lose the love of the English people. But Simier was a clever man – he knew Lord Robert was his enemy and he also knew that he was guarding a shocking secret. The time had come, he thought, to share that secret with the Queen.

'What? This cannot be true!'

Elizabeth's pale face turned a ghastly shade of grey.

'Oh, I assure you it is, your majesty,' said Simier. 'Lord Robert and Lettice Devereux, the widow of the Earl of Essex, have been married for almost a year.'

'He is under arrest!' cried the Queen. 'He must be sent to the Tower!'

Simier was shocked. 'Your majesty, I told you only so that you would see that this man is not to be trusted! Marriage, however, is not a crime...'

'Silence!' cried the Queen. 'I will be obeyed in this! You may go!'

The astonished Simier withdrew, leaving Elizabeth to her heart-broken fury. Stunned and bemused, the guards locked Lord Robert in a tower at Greenwich Palace, whilst arrangements were made for him to travel to the Tower of London. The Queen would see no one. Her ladies were sent away. She kept to her room alone.

'Your majesty.'

Sussex, the Lord Chamberlain, made his most elegant bow.

'What?' snapped Elizabeth. 'You are disturbing me.'

'It is most gracious of you to see me, ma'am,' said Sussex. He cleared his throat.

'Well? What have you to say?'

Sussex steeled himself. 'Your majesty, if you punish Lord Robert you will damage your reputation. You will appear jealous and mean and vengeful. He has not committed a crime and you will seem unjust if you treat him as if he has.'

Elizabeth turned away. Sussex could see the glint of tears in her eyes.

'Lettice Devereux is odious,' she said. 'I will not have her here at court.'

'No one suggests that you should,' said Sussex, gently.

'And I cannot bear to see... him! He must go to his house at Wanstead.'

'It will be arranged,' said Sussex, schooling his face so that she didn't see his utter relief.

'Thank you,' said Elizabeth, her voice tight. 'You may go.'

8
Carrying On

Only days later, the crisis was past. Robert pretended to be gravely ill, which gave the Queen an excuse to visit him and spend two days secretly at Wanstead whilst Lettice was elsewhere. She could not give up her old sweetheart and he still wanted to bask in her favour. She returned to London happy again, only to find that someone had attempted to shoot Simier, supposedly on Robert's orders. But she continued with the marriage negotiations. As long as they went on, the French remained her allies and not her enemies.

It was a pleasant summer evening some weeks later. The Queen was being rowed in the royal barge from London to the palace at Greenwich when suddenly, shots rang out and a rower slumped over his oar, hit in both arms. Whilst everyone else panicked, she flung her scarf to him to bind his wounds.

'Be of good cheer!' she cried. 'I will take care of you!'

Meanwhile, the marksman was found, a serving-man called Thomas Appletree. Far from attempting to kill either the Queen or Simier, he had been trying out his gun. He was still found guilty of creating a dangerous disturbance and sentenced to death. It was only a last-minute reprieve from the Queen which saved him from hanging and delighted the crowd that had gathered to watch. Though sometimes she allowed torture and execution, she could be merciful. Appletree had blundered badly but she would not see him hang for his mistake.

1580 Deptford

Elizabeth stared at the remarkably small ship that she was about to board to have dinner: the *Golden Hind*. Could this little vessel really have spent three years travelling all the way around the world? It was incredible. But she wasn't in the mood to disbelieve. She could only rejoice over the fact that she had had the guts to invest secretly in Francis Drake's enterprise, rash though it had been. Explorers were becoming more and more daring in their adventures – another of the court's young men, Walter Raleigh, was already muttering about sailing to the Americas – but Drake's expedition had been a very long shot. Now, however, he had brought glory to England by his remarkable achievement, the first Englishman ever to circumnavigate the globe.

Even better, he had a hold crammed with loot, silver and jewels captured mostly from Spanish ships he had raided. That, of course, had been part of the plan. Spain dominated international exploration and the oceans and it suited Elizabeth to contest this. She needed to keep the power of Spain in check, as England was still vulnerable to invasion and conquest. Dr John Dee, a mathematician and astronomer whom Elizabeth respected greatly, proposed that England had an equal right to build an empire in foreign territories, and Elizabeth was excited by his arguments. This could be a way to show Spain that England might be small but was still mighty – without the huge cost of going to war.

Spain was short of money too – and Philip couldn't dominate the world without it – so Drake's attacks on Spanish shipping were exactly what Elizabeth wanted. It was a neat way to keep Spain under control whilst building up England's finances. Just the capture of one Spanish merchant ship travelling home from the silver mines of Peru, resulted in a haul of 360,000 pesos in silver bars, coins and gold, not to mention a vast quantity of uncoined silver used as ballast!

It was not just silver and gold that Drake commandeered. Although much got broken, some priceless Chinese porcelain also survived to delight Elizabeth on Drake's return and, of course, there were other exotic goods brought from the lands Drake visited. Coconuts travelled particularly well and were considered so precious that they were turned into cups embellished with silver ornamentation.

The Spanish ambassador demanded the return of the treasure – as far as he was concerned, Drake was nothing but a pirate – but Elizabeth refused;

it was far too valuable a haul. No one must ever know, of course, that such plunder was what she had hoped for all along! She gave a share of the loot to Drake and others who had financed his voyage, and locked the rest away in the Tower.

Much to the disgust of the Spaniards, Francis Drake was even knighted. Cunningly, Elizabeth handed the sword for this task to the French envoy, thus making it look as if the French approved. All seemed to be going remarkably well but still, simmering away in the background, was the question of the Queen's marriage.

The Duke of Alençon had been busy with battles of his own but, pleased with his success, he decided to visit Elizabeth and urge her, once and for all, to marry him. If she seriously wanted to have a child, she was running out of time. The pair were walking in the gallery at Greenwich when they were approached by the French ambassador, wanting to know if he could give his master, the King of France, news that the marriage would take place.

Elizabeth turned to Alençon and kissed him. 'You may tell his Majesty that the Prince will be my husband,' she said. She took off one of her rings and placed it on his finger.

Elizabeth's favourite men were horrified. But Burghley knew better. The Queen was simply playing for time. The very next day, she sent the Duke a message explaining that she had spoken too hastily. On reflection, she was worried that marriage might kill her. She was too old to try to have a baby – she hoped he didn't want his love to be the cause of her death!

The Duke was thunder-struck – and now Elizabeth had to account for the three years she had kept him dangling in order to keep war with France at bay. Soon the Duke started threatening to form an alliance with Spain. Burghley found the solution: Alençon simply had to be paid enough to stop him doing so. Much to Elizabeth's disgust, it was done – at huge cost. But at least she had avoided war.

Meanwhile Elizabeth had other problems to contend with. Another major plot had been uncovered by the Queen's spy-master, Walsingham. It was led by a man called Anthony Babington, and Mary Queen of Scots was again involved. It was becoming clear that the Spanish hoped to assassinate Elizabeth and then invade and make Mary Queen.

Elizabeth began to live in fear of her life and as time went on that fear grew worse and worse. She began to behave in an extremely jumpy and nervous manner. On one occasion she fainted and remained unconscious for two hours; on another she was going to chapel when suddenly she took fright at something which she wouldn't explain. The shock was so severe that she had to return to her bedchamber. She was seen to be particularly irritable with her spy-master, Walsingham. One day, he said something so annoying that she tore off her shoe and threw it at him.

Walsingham had believed for years that Mary Queen of Scots did very little else except plot against Elizabeth, but it was remarkably difficult to catch her red-handed, despite his highly effective network of spies both at home and in foreign courts. He was now playing a waiting game. One of his spies had discovered that, rather than being home-brewed, beer was sent weekly into Chartley, the house where Mary was currently held under arrest. A plan was therefore devised to persuade Mary and her supporters to conceal their letters in a water-proof bag in the beer keg's stopper. They fell for the trick, believing it was a cunning way to pass secret messages, and Walsingham could now intercept and decode all the letters that passed to and from Mary. But he had to wait for one that clearly betrayed her guilt.

Meanwhile, Elizabeth also had to wait – at continual risk of death. It was a huge strain on her nerves.The Privy Council was at least as concerned as Walsingham, and were growing impatient. In 1584 they passed the Bond of Association in an attempt to stop people conspiring with Mary. They could guess only too well what would happen to them if she took power! The Bond meant that they would pursue to the death, not only anyone guilty of plotting against Elizabeth, but also whoever the plotters supported as her replacement, whether they knew about the plot or not. This meant that Mary could be executed for a plot to put her on the throne, even if she could not be shown to be personally involved. Still, however, everyone was waiting on Walsingham and his spy-ring.

At last in 1586, Walsingham had his proof – a coded letter from Mary writing of forces inside and outside the country, of six gentlemen about to do 'their work', and of her own escape from Chartley. He pounced. The conspirators were quickly rounded up. Mary was sent to Fotheringhay Castle to be tried for treason. She still protested her innocence, claiming that the vital, incriminating letter had not been written by her. It was true that Walsingham had added a post-script in an attempt to get Babington to name his associates, but the body of the letter was untouched.

It made no difference anyway. Mary had been proved to be in correspondence with Anthony Babington for at least two years although she had claimed she did not know him. Her days were numbered.

9
Griefs and Triumphs

1587 Greenwich Palace

'Your majesty, it is six weeks since your cousin Mary was found guilty of treason and sentenced to death – and still you will not sign her death warrant,' said the Lord Admiral, Lord Howard of Effingham. 'The people are restless. Rumours abound. They say that she has broken out of prison, that the City has been set on fire, that a Spanish army has arrived in Wales! If this goes on, we could have riots! The people need to know that the Queen of Scots is dead – that you are safe and secure and there is no threat of a foreign army invading and taking over.'

The Queen snorted. 'There is always a threat of that, Lord Howard!' she said. 'Killing my cousin will make it more likely, not less. What is there to lose once she is dead? They might just as well invade and stick my head on a pole. At least with her alive, they fear what I might do to her!'

'I can only tell you that the public temper is becoming dangerous,' Lord Howard persisted. 'And you have always been much loved by the common people. They will not, however, stand much more of this suspense.'

'I see I must strike or be stricken,' said Elizabeth, wearily, 'though if I strike, it is at one who is a crowned Queen and should never be struck.'

'She would have struck you,' insisted Lord Howard. 'She has tried to have you killed – several times!'

Elizabeth sighed deeply. 'I will sign the warrant,' she said. 'Let secretary Davison bring it.'

On 9th February 1587, Elizabeth returned from her morning ride to the pealing of London's bells. Mary Queen of Scots, was dead, defiant to the last. She had worn a blood-red slip, the sign of the martyr, and when her head was finally held up to the spectators, it fell to the floor, just a wig being left in the executioner's hand. The great beauty who had drawn so many men to their ruin had shorn grey hair, not the glowing locks of her portraits. Elizabeth took the news of Mary's death calmly and then shut herself in her rooms and burst into a terrible fit of weeping. When her tears were spent, she sent for Lord Howard and Davison. She was furious.

'I never meant you to take that warrant and deliver it,' she told Davison. 'I wanted it held in readiness, that is all! I might never have needed to use it. A Queen is dead and it is your fault! You have made me an object of hatred!'

'Indeed, your majesty, it is not so,' said Lord Howard soothingly. 'The people will respect you for this. She had been tried and found guilty.'

'Get out of my sight,' the Queen raged. 'And you,' she said to Davison, 'you I will see hanged.'

Fortunately, Elizabeth could not have Davison executed. He had done nothing wrong and no one would support her in her hysterical fury. Burghley was very troubled. He had never known her behave with such arrogance and injustice, but he was a wise man and he understood – she could not bear to take the responsibility for killing her cousin herself. It was easier to blame someone else for misunderstanding her instructions. The least said, the soonest mended.

There were enough troubles looming to deal with. Elizabeth might be safe from secret plots on her life but Burghley was sure Philip II would now attack openly. He was Mary Tudor's husband – he had been the King of England. With the Queen of Scots out of the way, he had nothing to lose by invading except money – and if he captured the English throne, it would be a rich prize which he could bestow on one of his daughters. He had the Pope's blessing. Elizabeth had been thrown out of the Catholic church and the Pope had made it clear that anyone who tried to de-throne her was on a mission from God. At the same time, Philip's nephew, the Duke of Parma, looked set to gain control of the Netherlands which, as Spain also had control of Portugal, made its empire colossal. England would complete the set.

Sir Francis Drake, acting with brilliant initiative on information gained from Dutch sailors, managed to delay the Spanish invasion for a year by attacking the Spanish fleet in the harbour at Cadiz. He took them by surprise, sailing right into the harbour. The Spanish fired cannon from land but did little damage, and battle raged all night. In the morning, Drake withdrew, leaving chaos. As they sailed away, the English attacked every Spanish vessel they encountered, finally destroying or capturing over one hundred vessels.

Even so, Elizabeth knew this only gave her a breathing space, and, sure enough, on 19th July 1588 at three o'clock, watchers in Cornwall saw the sight that everyone dreaded: the Spanish Armada, a crescent of huge ships built high like castles and towers, advancing slowly across the churning sea.

1588 Richmond – Invasion

Elizabeth drew in her breath and drummed the arm of her chair with her long fingers.

'So,' she said. 'Finally, they are here.'

'Indeed, your majesty. And would you have us move to Windsor?' asked Lord Burghley.

'What, run away to a castle in fear?' said Elizabeth. 'I don't think that would improve the confidence of the people! No – we have a fleet which is second to none and I have great faith in my Admiral, Lord Howard. We will await developments before we turn tail and run!'

'Your majesty, I was only suggesting as a matter of caution...' But Burghley caught the steely look in her eye and fell silent.

'Thank you, you may go,' said Elizabeth. 'Keep me informed of anything and everything.'

'News will come slowly, your majesty – it is all happening way out at sea.'

'I am well aware of that,' said Elizabeth. 'But I want to know what happens as soon as we hear. Now leave me, please.'

Burghley left quietly. Once again, he was impressed. If things went badly, Elizabeth could lose not only her crown but her life – and England was so tiny in comparison with the might of the Spanish Empire. But Elizabeth didn't seem remotely cowed.

Elizabeth, meanwhile, stared out of the window, wishing she could see all the way out to the Channel where by now surely, the two fleets were engaged in battle. She had done all she felt she could afford to equip her navy. Now she must rely on the skill and judgement of her Admiral and the devotion of her subjects. Whether Catholic or Protestant, she knew they didn't want to be ruled by Spain. It was hard but she was practical – there was no point in worrying.

1588 Tilbury

Elizabeth sat bareheaded, strikingly dressed in white on a white horse. Over her usual finery she wore a steel corselet. A page followed her carrying a helmet with white feather plumes, the Earl of Ormonde strode before her carrying a sword and Lord Robert, now Lieutenant General of her forces, marched at her side. When she reached the massed ranks of soldiers, Elizabeth walked along the lines, smiling encouragingly, displaying a confidence she did not feel.

No one was quite sure how the sea battle was going and even though she'd heard that the Spanish had sustained considerable losses, the Armada was the least of her fears – it was, after all, only a defensive escort to the Duke of Parma's huge army which was advancing from the Netherlands. Elizabeth had wanted to go to the coast but Lord Robert had advised against it, instead suggesting that she came no nearer the sea than Tilbury, on the north bank of the Thames, where she could inspire the troops by reviewing them. And so that was what she was doing, keeping a brave face, refusing to give in to the thought that by the end of the day, she might no longer be Queen. She addressed the men, telling them that though she had but the body of a weak and feeble woman, she had the heart and stomach of a king, a king of England at that, and they told each other that they would die for her.

That night, whilst Elizabeth was dining at the camp, news came that the Duke of Parma was embarking with his troops and that the Armada was re-grouping for a return strike.

'Well, then,' said Elizabeth to Walsingham who was sitting beside her. 'I cannot return to London now. It is a matter of honour to stay with my troops in case anything is attempted.'

Walsingham nodded sagely. 'You must do as you see fit,' he said, 'but I counsel you that the most honourable course is to preserve your life for those who love you and fight in your service. If you are captured, men will have risked their lives for nothing.'

Elizabeth looked at him gravely. 'I will think this over,' she said, 'and decide in the morning.'

'A wise choice,' agreed Walsingham. 'Things may look very different tomorrow.'

Privately, he wondered if there had ever been such a courageous queen throughout the whole course of history.

Victory! Elizabeth almost wept with relief. The story was astonishing. England's modern ships which had seemed so defenceless against the huge Spanish ships, had won! They had triumphed through speed, ease of steering, superb fire power and sheer good luck.

A series of smaller battles ended in the decisive battle at Gravelines after English fire-ships had forced the Spanish ships to move from their anchorage at Calais. The slaughter of the Spanish was dreadful. When one ship heeled over, blood was seen pouring out of its scuppers. In the end, the Spanish fled, trying to make their way up to Scotland and the west coast of Ireland. English ships pursuing them passed the bodies of the mules and horses they had thrown overboard to try to reduce their weight. But the English didn't need to catch them. Instead the weather did. Storms, shipwrecks and finally the unfriendly Irish and Scots meant that in the end, of thirty thousand Spanish who set out, fewer than half returned to Spain. The English lost only sixty men.

But out of this great triumph, and the end of the Spanish threat, came terrible personal grief.

Lord Robert had suffered a low fever ever since his return after the Armada victory and Elizabeth recommended that he visit Buxton in Derbyshire to take the spa waters. He got as far as Cornbury Park in Oxfordshire. There he died, aged just fifty-four years old.

Elizabeth refused to see anyone. Her anguish was dreadful. Day followed day and still the Queen would see no one, devastated by grief. In the end Burghley ordered her door to be broken open. The Queen, tough as ever, pulled herself together. Life had to go on. She had to rule. She also had to be practical, and money was always an issue. She seized Lord Robert's castle at Kenilworth and all his lands in Warwickshire for the crown. But when she died, fifteen years later, in her jewelled casket of most precious things was found, labelled in her distinctive writing, 'His Last Letter'.

10

Essex and the End

1599 London

Elizabeth regarded the excitable, handsome young man sternly.

'No,' she said. 'I disagree. I will send Sir William Knollys as Deputy in the Irish campaign, not Sir George Carew. Kindly have the courtesy to accept my judgement.'

Robert Devereux, Earl of Essex did not take the hint. He had been her favourite for over a decade, taking the place of Lord Robert Dudley despite being the son of Lettice Devereux, Robert's odious wife. The Queen was Essex's senior by over thirty years, and he was inclined to think her love for him bullet-proof. He had even taken over the job that Lord Robert had had for so many years – the Master of the Horse, a role that brought him into constant contact with the Queen. She was a woman addicted to romance, he thought. She, after all, had suggested to Mr William Shakespeare, the well-known actor and playwright who often performed with The Lord Chamberlain's Company at court, that he create a play about his elderly comic character Sir John Falstaff falling in love – though Falstaff had only appeared previously in plays about war. Essex was sure the Queen doted on him, so he felt he could do as he liked. Consequently, he petulantly turned his back, far too confident of her affection to realise that she also demanded respect.

Elizabeth had never been known for her patience and as she approached old age, she had become increasingly irritable. Infuriated by Essex's rudeness, she slapped him round the head.

'Go and be hanged!' she shouted.

A wiser man would have apologised immediately. Instead, Essex clapped his hand to his sword hilt.

'This is an outrage!' he shouted. 'I wouldn't stand for this from Henry VIII himself!'

Shocked gasps filled the room. Lord Nottingham had the sense to act. He rushed forward and stopped Essex from drawing the sword. Had the young man done so, he could not have escaped execution. Such an obvious act of treachery could not have been ignored, even in one of whom the Queen was so fond.

But Essex did not learn his lesson. He was an arrogant young man and believed that Elizabeth doted on him so much that he could get away with anything. Unlike the men Elizabeth had favoured in the past, he had little political sense and no real understanding of Elizabeth. Old and fond of him she might be, but she had never let affection get the better of her wisdom. Essex escaped this time, saved by Lord Nottingham's prompt action, but it was only a short time before his rash behaviour doomed him.

Despite having seen off the Spanish threat, Elizabeth was far from free of trouble with her neighbours. Ireland was the source of nightmares. Elizabeth was supposed to be its Queen, but now the Earl of Tyrone was leading a rebellion. Essex insisted that he would be the best man to sort out the problem and some of Elizabeth's advisors agreed – so he was sent. Unfortunately, from the moment he arrived in Ireland he disobeyed his instructions and tackled the problem in his own way – which was a complete disaster. He wasted thousands of pounds and men, and completely failed to get Tyrone to surrender. Despite being told to stay where he was and continue his duties, Essex, panicking, made a mad dash home. At the end of his reckless journey, supported by a group of gallant but misguided friends, he burst into the Queen's bedchamber, even his face splattered with mud. He threw himself on his knees, frantically kissing her fingers. She was not properly dressed and didn't even have on her red wig to cover her grey hair.

'My Lord Essex!' she said, astounded. She had had no idea he wasn't in Ireland.

'Your majesty, I have come to explain...' Essex begged.

'Then you can explain to my Privy Council,' she said. 'For now, please withdraw and make yourself presentable. I will see you when I am ready.'

For once, Essex had the sense to do as he was told.

'I thank God that after such trouble and storms abroad, I have found a sweet calm at home,' he was heard to say as he left.

But all was not calm. Storms still lay ahead. Essex was not charged with treason, even though he had suggested to Tyrone that Ireland could rule itself. Instead, he was put under house arrest and so he remained for many months. His mother sensibly did not protest. His sister, however, sent a very rash letter to Elizabeth, worded so disrespectfully that it made matters worse.

Meanwhile, Essex became more and more unstable, convinced that the courtiers were working against him but that he was very popular with the ordinary people. Fired up by the support of rebellious friends, it was clear that he was becoming dangerous. He had convinced himself that Sir Robert Cecil, who was Elizabeth's new first secretary and the son of Lord Burghley, was plotting against the Queen and himself.

The Queen summoned Essex to the Privy Council to explain his behaviour, which looked suspiciously like that of someone planning a rebellion. Claiming he was ill, he refused to go. Instead he led his supporters in an attempt to overthrow the court and declare Cecil and his supporters to be traitors, thinking that the people of London would support him.

They didn't. Essex's revolt was an embarrassing disaster. When, soaked with sweat, he tried to change his shirt at Sheriff Smythe's house, the sheriff promptly disappeared out of the back door. In the end, Essex and his closest supporter, the Earl of Southampton, fled to the roof of Essex House.

The end was swift. The Lord Admiral sent by boat for cannons and gunpowder from the Tower. He said he would give Essex an hour to let the ladies leave the house before he blew it up – unless he gave himself up. The barrels of gunpowder were being unloaded on the lawn when Essex agreed. He and Southampton were sent to the Tower.

'A messenger has come. May he have entry?'

The Privy Chamber, full of music seconds ago, fell utterly silent.

The Queen nodded to the servant and the messenger was let in. Everyone stood still, eyes riveted on the man who flung himself on one knee before the Queen. It was obvious what he had come to say.

'Your majesty, the sentence upon the Earl of Essex has been carried out,' he said.

No one moved. No one spoke. It was as if no one could breathe. And then music once more filled the silence. The Queen had begun to play again.

In days to come, her grief at the loss of her young favourite was very real. But to the French Ambassador she told what was on her heart.

'In such cases, there is no middle course,' she said. 'We must lay aside mercy and adopt extreme measures.'

There were those, however, who thought she never recovered from her decision to execute the Earl of Essex.

1603 The End

Elizabeth was exhausted. She hated the thought of retiring to bed but scarcely had the energy to walk. Once again, she sank down onto the floor cushions in her Privy Chamber. She felt as if she would never move again and yet she was restless and uncomfortable. She knew she had a fever, was constantly thirsty and her throat was sore and full of phlegm. She didn't want to do anything and had no appetite. She would drift into sleep and then wake an hour or so later, dogged by gloomy thoughts.

It was two years since Essex's execution and all her other closest male advisors were dead. She thought fondly of Burghley, her First Secretary for so many years. Dying, he had been unable to feed himself, and she had gently fed him gruel with a spoon. How she missed him! His son, Sir Robert Cecil, had taken his place but it was not the same. And of course, after all these years, she still missed Lord Robert.

She was sixty-nine and the doctors had said that she could live much longer, but she was weary and becoming forgetful. Her mind, always so alert, was clouded. And she sensed that the people too were weary of their old, frail Queen. Fresh blood was needed – but the question still remained – who?

Sir Robert Cecil entered the room.

'Madam, to content the people you must go to bed,' he said firmly.

Elizabeth smiled wryly. She was troublesome where she was. It would be better now for her to be out of the way. But she rallied and addressed Cecil in her usual playful yet firm manner.

'Little man, little man,' she said. 'The word *must* is not to be used to princes. If your father lived you would not have dared say it.'

Only a few days later, Elizabeth was so faint that she had to be carried to bed. She revived a little and asked for some meat broth but it was clear that she was dying. An abscess in her throat burst and she could scarcely swallow or speak. Still the question of the succession remained unanswered. She could only gesture with a hand.

'Would it please you for James, the King of Scotland, the son of Mary Queen of Scots, to be the next king of England?' she was asked.

She raised her hand. 'Yes.'

Throughout London, the bells hung silently in the churches, as Elizabeth lay dying. Had there ever been a reign more glorious? At quarter to three on the morning of 24th March, 1603, Elizabeth's head, always so haughty and upright, slumped sideways. The survivor of so many plots and threats was gone.

She was buried in Westminster Abbey next to her sister Mary. The new King James had a splendid tomb built in her honour, just as he did for his mother, Mary Queen of Scots. And so to this day, Elizabeth lies with the two women who would have gladly seen her dead – but she outlived them both.

THE BRITISH ISLES IN ELIZABETH'S REIGN
SCOTLAND
Lochleven
Edinburgh
Fotheringhay
Dublin
Kenilworth
Woodstock
Hatfield
Windsor
London
Greenwich
Tilbury

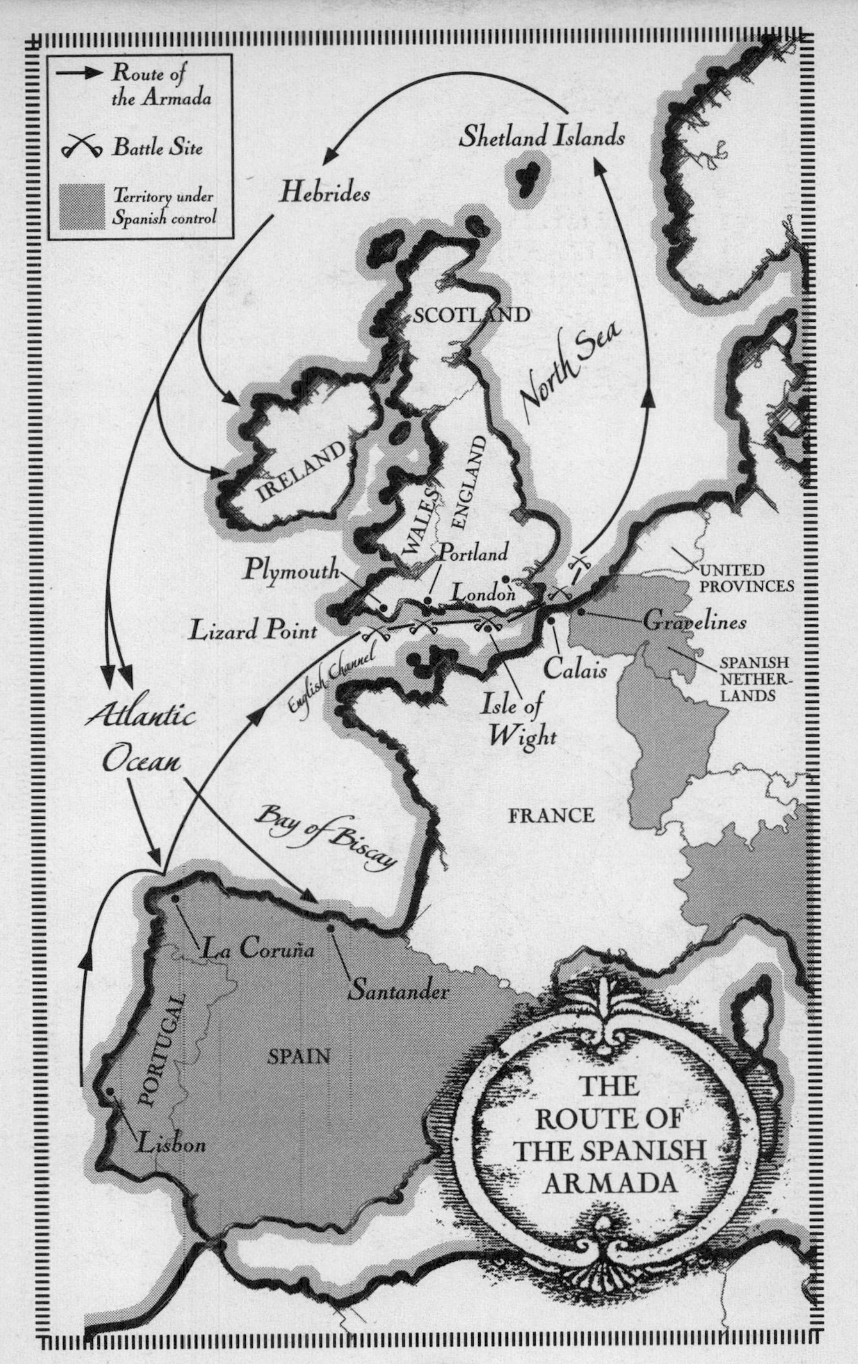

Route of the Armada
Battle Site
Territory under Spanish control
Shetland Islands
Hebrides
SCOTLAND
North Sea
IRELAND
ENGLAND
WALES
Portland
Plymouth
London
Lizard Point
English Channel
UNITED PROVINCES
Gravelines
Calais
SPANISH NETHERLANDS
Isle of Wight
Atlantic Ocean
Bay of Biscay
FRANCE
La Coruña
Santander
PORTUGAL
SPAIN
Lisbon
THE ROUTE OF THE SPANISH ARMADA

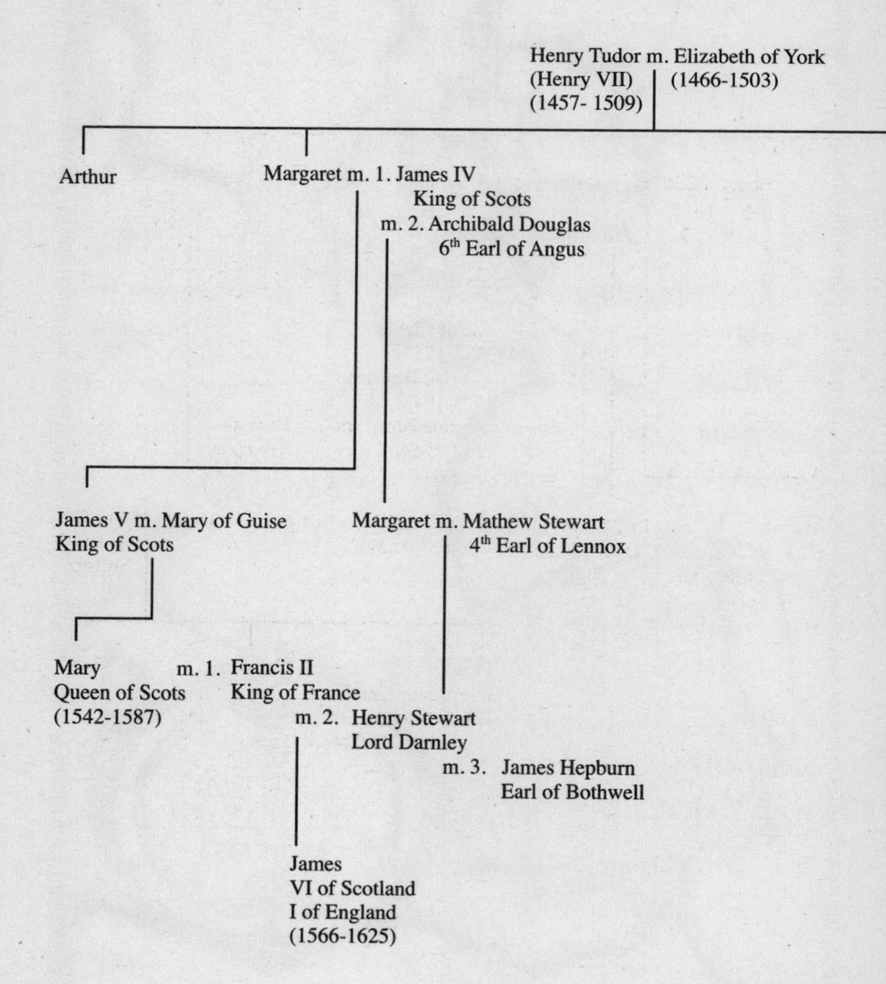
Henry Tudor m. Elizabeth of York
(Henry VII)
(1466-1503)
(1457- 1509)
Arthur
Margaret m. 1. James IV
King of Scots
m. 2. Archibald Douglas
6th Earl of Angus
James V m. Mary of Guise
King of Scots
Margaret m. Mathew Stewart
4th Earl of Lennox
Mary
Queen of Scots
(1542-1587)
m. 1. Francis II
King of France
m. 2. Henry Stewart
Lord Darnley
m. 3. James Hepburn
Earl of Bothwell
James
VI of Scotland
I of England
(1566-1625)

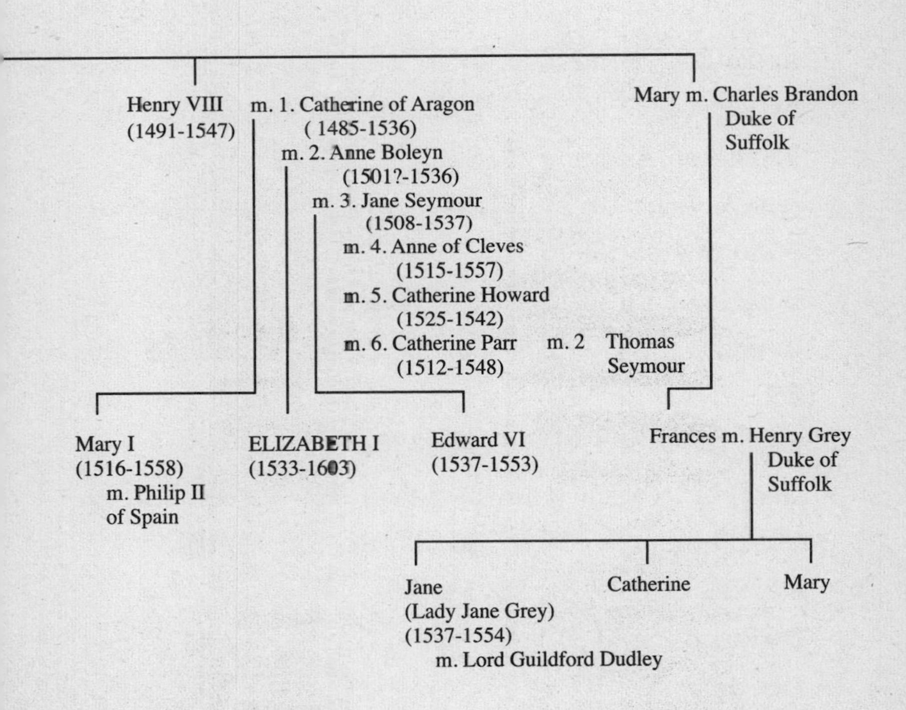

Note: dates given are those of birth and death.

Index